The
Dinosaur
Coast

Fist published by High Tide Publishing, 2015.
Reprinted with amendments, 2019.
Published in association with The North York Moors
National Park Authority, Scarborough Museums Trust and
Hidden Horizons.

A CIP catalogue record for this book is available from the
British Library

ISBN 978-0-9933646-0-0

Designed by David Hurley
Printed and bound in Great Britain by Adverset,
Scarborough

To order copies of this and other High Tide publications visit

www.hightidepublishing.co.uk/shop

Retailers wishing to stock or restock any of our publications
should email

hightidepublishing@btinternet.com

The Dinosaur Coast

Yorkshire Rocks, Fossils and Landscape

Roger Osborne

Contents

Welcome to

W elcome to this special pocket guide to Yorkshire's famous Dinosaur Coast. This is a completely new edition of our 2001 guide, aimed at both new and existing readers. If you are a visitor or a resident, an occasional walker or an avid fossil hunter, this book will enrich your experience of this beautiful coastline.

The stretch of coast from the Tees to Flamborough Head is one of the most stunning landscapes in Britain. The towering cliffs, secret coves, lovely villages and sweeping sandy beaches have been drawing visitors for centuries. But as well as the beauties of the landscape, the Dinosaur Coast carries an amazing story, which you can uncover with help of this guide.

A section through the coast

The rough sketch below of the Dinosaur Coast shows how rocks are stacked in layers. The strata slope gradually towards the south so the older shales of Lower Jurassic age outcrop in the north. Sandstones of the Middle Jurassic and Upper Jurassic limestones dominate the central area, with younger Cretaceous chalk in the south. A layer of glacial mud was added in the last ice age.

Variety of rocks

The column opposite shows the changing rock types on the Dinosaur Coast from the oldest Redcar Mudstone to the youngest Cretaceous chalk. You can use this as a guide to the sections in this book and to the rocks of the coast.

We take you on a journey from north to south and through geological time. The Lower Jurassic rocks are a mix of shales and sandstones, full of fossil shells and the occasional marine reptile. In the Middle Jurassic period this was a coastal delta, with

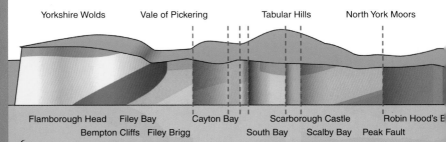

Yorkshire Wolds   Vale of Pickering   Tabular Hills   North York Moors

Flamborough Head   Filey Bay   Cayton Bay   Scarborough Castle   Robin Hood's B
Bempton Cliffs   Filey Brigg   South Bay   Scalby Bay   Peak Fault

Upper Jurassic	Cretaceous chalk
	Kimmeridge Clay
	Upper Calcareous Grit
	Malton Oolite
	Middle Calc Grit
	Hambleton Oolite
	Lower Calc Grit
	Oxford Clay
	Osgodby Sandstone
Middle Jurassic	Cornbrash
	Moor Grit
	Scarborough Limestone
	Saltwick and Cloughton Formations
	Dogger
Lower Jurassic	Whitby Mudstone (inc Alum and Jet Rock)
	Cleveland Ironstone
	Staithes Sandstone
	Redcar Mudstone

began with clay formation, before a tranquil lime-rich sea created the conditions for massive deposits of chalk, probably around 700 metres deep.

All this will become clearer as you explore the following pages. So tuck this book into your pocket and head out to the coast to see for yourself.

More guidance is at hand from Scarborough-based Hidden Horizons (www.hiddenhorizons.co.uk) in the form of fossil hunts and guided walks. We hope you enjoy this book and the places where it takes you.

plants and dinosaur footprints preserved in sandstones. In the Upper Jurassic a warm tropical sea was home to corals, sponges, sea anemones and ammonites. These are preserved in limestones, interbedded with grits. The Cretaceous period

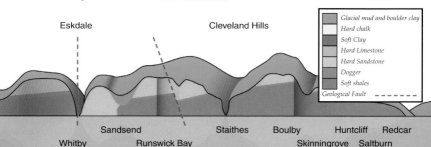

	Glacial mud and boulder clay
	Hard chalk
	Soft Clay
	Hard Limestone
	Hard Sandstone
	Dogger
	Soft shales
Geological Fault	- - - - -

Eskdale   Cleveland Hills

Whitby   Sandsend   Runswick Bay   Staithes   Boulby   Skinningrove   Huntcliff   Saltburn   Redcar

Saltburn to Sands

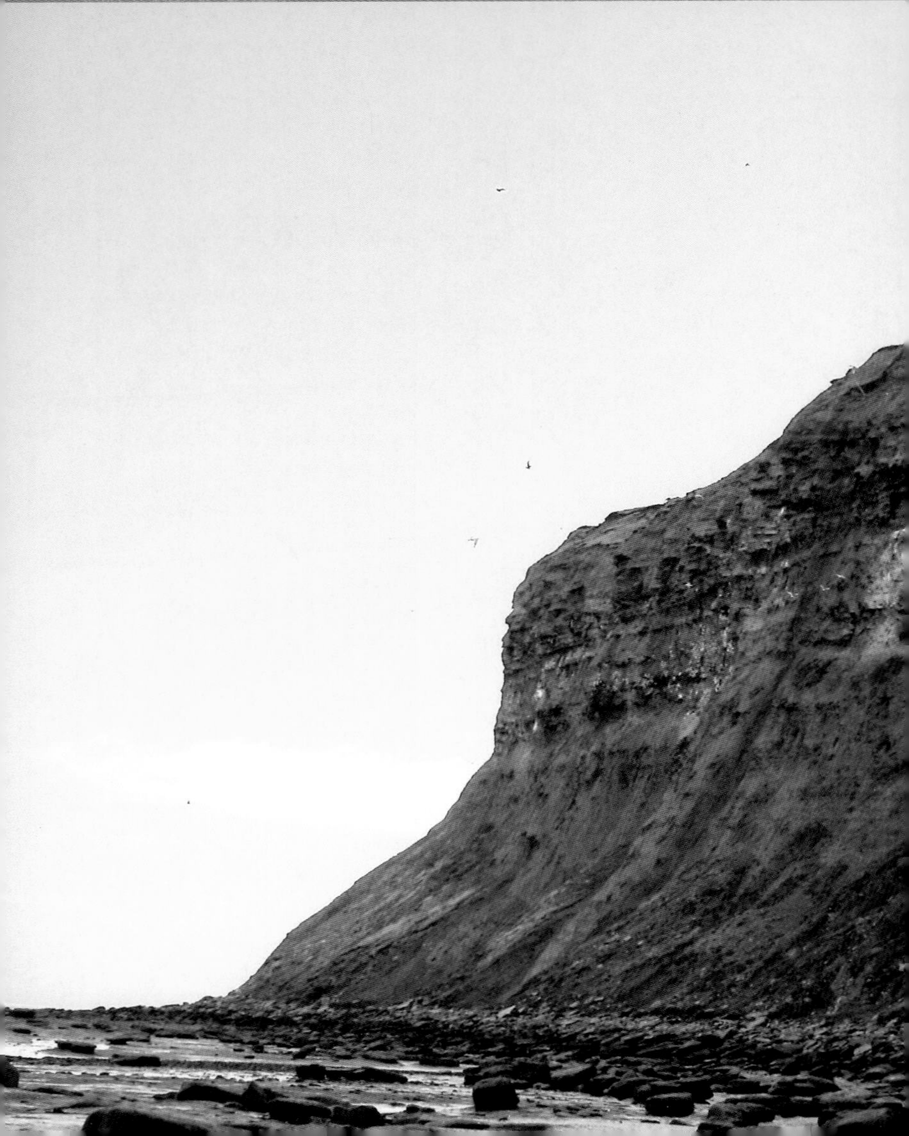

The map shows:

TEES

altburn-by-the-Sea
Loftus
gh
sborough
Whitby

AR AND
LAND   R Esk   Robin Hood's Bay
Goathland

The Dinosaur Coast begins in dramatic fashion as the great cliffs at Saltburn rise above the flat plain of the Tees Valley. From here to Kettleness are some of the highest cliffs in England, providing spectacular scenery, mineral riches and havens for a diversity of wildlife. Cut into the cliffs are narrow gorges that provide shelter for villages at Skinningrove, Staithes and Runswick. The exception is the sweeping bay at Sandsend, probably formed by a river that was blocked during the last ice age.

Saltburn to Boulby

This stretch of coast contains the highest cliffs anywhere on the east coast of England. From Huntcliff to Hummersea and Boulby the Jurassic rocks tower above the sea. At Skinningrove the line of cliffs is broken by Kilton Beck cutting through to form a flat valley floor. This is the southern edge of the great iron mining district of East Cleveland which drove the industrialisation of Britain. Vast quantities of alum were extracted at both Hummersea and Boulby, leaving huge abandoned quarries along the coast.

Saltburn

Saltburn sees the beginning of the Jurassic rocks of the Dinosaur Coast. The Victorian town of Saltburn sits on a clifftop of glacial clay that covers the Tees valley. Clay cliffs stretch all the way north to Redcar and form the conical hill of Cat Nab.

South of the Ship Inn the towering face of Huntcliff dominates the view. The cliffs are made of Lower Jurassic grey Redcar Mudstone topped by Cleveland Ironstone. This hard cap makes the cliffs near-vertical. The cliffs are topped by a sloping grassy layer of glacial till.

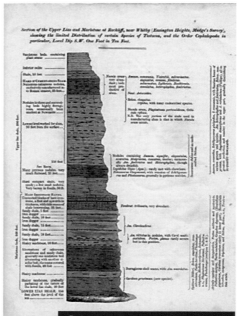

❶ The famous cliff lift at Saltburn carries passengers from the shore up the sharply sloping mud cliffs to the town.

❸ The landmark hill of Cat Nab is a conical pile of red glacial mud isolated by streams and by the two roads leading south from Saltburn.

❷ This section from Louis Hunton's 1836 paper was a landmark in science. The rock strata in the cliff on the left are minutely described and the fossils limited to each layer are named on the right. See over the page for more on Louis Hunton.

Cleveland iron

The East Cleveland iron mines fed the blast furnaces of Teesside from the 1850s until the last mine at North Skelton closed in 1964. The iron ore came from six seams within the Cleveland Ironstone Formation. At Eston the Main Seam, 3.6 metres thick, lies directly on the Pecten Seam, 1.2 metres thick, making this one of the best sources of iron ore in the country. Ironstone was mined across East Cleveland and in the Esk Valley inland from Whitby.

CLEVELANDS IRONSTONE MINES

Railways Standard Gauge ——
          Narrow gauge - - - -

MILES

④ At low tide at Saltburn the Redcar Mudstone forms a huge flat area washed by the sea. The boulders have toppled down from the ironstone layers above.

Skinningrove

Built in the so-called 'iron valley' Skinningrove is a wonderful example of an industrial village. Ironstone seams are at sea-level, allowing drift mines to be driven down through the sides of the valley, while the accessible shore was ideal for taking ore out by ship. The steel industry kept going even after the iron mines closed. The works at Carlin How, above Skinningrove, produce high quality rolled steel.

1 Cleveland Iron Mining Museum at Skinningrove is actually an old iron mine. Here you can go underground and see the tough working conditions faced by miners including appalling circumstances in which children worked.

2 The iron-rich waters of Kilton Beck at Skinningrove. The exposed seams make the run-off waters toxic to plant life, so steps are being taken to purify the waters naturally.

3 Ironstone in the cliffs at Skinningrove. Boats took ore from here to Middlesbrough before the railway was built.

Boulby

Boulby Cliffs are among the highest in England, rising 203 metres above the North Sea. The southward dip of the rock strata has brought younger rocks into the cliffs. Here the hard cap of the rocks is made up of Middle Jurassic sandstones from the Saltwick formation. Under these are the soft shales of the Whitby Mudstone formation which is present along most of the northern part of the Dinosaur Coast.

Hummersea

In 1836 Louis Hunton, son of the manager of the alum works at Hummersea, published a scientific paper that proved a milestone in geology. Hunton studied the local cliffs and saw that certain fossils occurred only in certain rock strata. Before then there was only a vague idea about the relation of fossils to strata; after Hunton it was possible to match the ages of rocks in different locations through their characteristic fossils.

Bivalves

The Cleveland Ironstone is packed with fossil bivalves. The Pecten and Avicula seams are named for bivalve groups. These group names have been superseded by the modern names shown here. The rock is a yellow sandstone with a fairly coarse texture; the fossils stand out as smooth hard objects within this matrix.

❹ These huge alum quarries below the clifftops at Boulby were dug out by hand over two centuries. The soft alum shale lies below the hard bands of rock visible on the left, with piles of slag in the centre of the picture.

Oxytoma (formerly Avicula) inaequivalvis

Pseudopecten equivalis

Oxytoma (formerly Avicula) cygnipes

Staithes to Runswick

One of the most picturesque parts of the coast, this section takes in the villages of Staithes and Runswick Bay as well as the cove at Port Mulgrave. The geology here is fascinating with huge cliff exposures of three major formations of Lower Jurassic rocks. Staithes Sandstone and Cleveland Ironstone are capped by Whitby Mudstone and, from Port Mulgrave south, by Middle Jurassic sandstones. Boundaries between these formations are clearly visible in the cliffs. Old trackways and jetties show how these rocks were once exploited for minerals.

Staithes

This beautiful village is built on steep slopes overlooking a small bay. Access to the sea is possible here because of Staithes Beck cutting a deep gorge through the hard layers of Staithes Sandstone. The headland of Cowbar Nab provides shelter for the boats using the beck and harbour, while cliffs on the east side show Cleveland Ironstone. The foot of the Nab roughly marks the point at which the older Redcar formation is overlain by the Staithes Sandstone. The boundary is marked by a distinctive rock known as the Oyster Bed.

❶ Staithes Beck cuts a steep gully through the hard layers of rock.
❷ The distinctive head of Cowbar Nab is made of hard Staithes Sandstone emerging out of the softer Redcar Mudstone below.

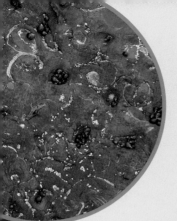

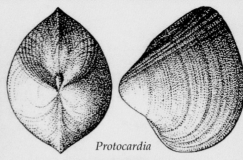

Protocardia

The Oyster Bed on the
scar below Cowbar Nab is
packed with fossil bivalves
including Protocardia,
Oxytoma, Pseudopecten
and the well-known
Gryphaea or Devil's Toenail.
Pleuroceras ammonites are
also found at Staithes.

Pleuroceras

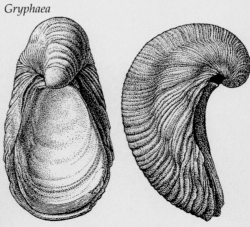

Gryphaea

East side cliffs

The towering cliffs on the eastern side of Staithes show a beautiful section through Lower Jurassic rocks. The upper part of the Staithes Sandstone is at the bottom, topped by the younger beds of the Cleveland Ironstone formation. The hard seams of ironstone stand out in the upper part of the cliff. The sandstones were formed in shallow seas and show signs of being reworked by tides and storm surges while they were being formed.

Going east and south the ironstone seams are progressively lower in the cliffs. Adit mines were cut into the seams from the beach and the remains of a tramway, used to take iron ore out to ships, are visible.

Port Mulgrave

In 1857 Charles Palmer built a harbour here to ship iron ore from his mine to furnaces at Jarrow. As the mine on the site was worked out, Palmer dug a tunnel through

to his mine at Grinkle. The harbour was abandoned in 1916 when the Grinkle mine was connected to the inland railway.

The rocks at Port Mulgrave are quite different from Staithes as the ironstone gives way to the Whitby Mudstone formation. Jet has been quarried along the shoreline.

❶ Hard seams of Ironstone stand out in the high cliffs above the east side of Staithes.

2 In the early 20th century the jetties at Port Mulgrave were used to load iron ore onto ships. The ore was brought via a tunnel running from Grinkle mine down near to the shore. The harbour has been filled in and is now used by small fishing boats.

3 At Runswick Bay the soft shales of Whitby Mudstone are capped by a hard layer of Middle Jurassic rocks from the Saltwick formation. The divide is clearly visible; in the distance is the quarried headland at Kettleness.

Runswick Bay

This open sandy cove has been created by a series of becks cutting down through the hard cap of the Middle Jurassic rocks into the soft shales of Whitby Mudstone. Mud and boulder clay left by the last ice age have affected the course of the becks but the overall effect is a soft curved bay. Cleveland Ironstone forms the scar in the southern part of the bay and at Kettleness.

4 The cliffs behind the cottages at Runswick clearly show hard Middle Jurassic sandstone slabs sitting on top of soft Lower Jurassic shales.

Kettleness to Sandsend

The coast here is dominated by the magnificent headlands of Kettleness and Sandsend Ness before sweeping down to the long sandy beach at Sandsend itself. The effects of the alum trade are more obvious here than anywhere else on the coast, with vast areas resembling a sterile, fascinating moonscape. There is an excellent display of rock types and industrial remains at Sandsend and wonderful views from the cliff tops all along the coast.

Kettleness

The headland at Kettleness is like a cake with a bite taken out. The bite shows the millions of tons of alum shale and overburden that were quarried out and processed here. The alum shales are part of the Whitby Mudstone Formation which forms the upper part of the cliffs, overlain by hard Middle Jurassic sandstones. The platform that remains where the shale has been removed is made of Cleveland Ironstone. The headland was the site of a Roman signal station, one of a chain along the Yorkshire Coast.

Sandsend

The beach at Sandsend owes its existence to a river that has disappeared. The river cut a wide valley down through the hard layers of Middle Jurassic rock and through the Dogger into the soft alum shales beneath. When the last ice age ended around 11,000 years ago millions of tons of mud and clay were dumped along the coast, filling the river valley and blocking its access to the sea. The low cliffs at Sandsend are made of glacial mud – clearly visible from the beach and the road.

1 This view from Runswick Bay shows the huge chunks taken out of Kettleness headland by quarrying and processing alum. All this was removed by hand and processed and shipped out from this site.

2 Ammonites embedded in the wave-cut scar at the north end of Sandsend are often coloured gold by iron pyrites. The scar is a flat area of Whitby Mudstone.

3 The acres of loose grey stone on the headlands at Sandsend and Kettleness are the remnants of alum shale burned in stacks on the floor of the quarries and then leached to extract the alum-rich liquor.

Sandsend Ness

This is one of the most fascinating areas of the Dinosaur Coast, combining geology, history, industrial archaeology, railways and natural history in one headland. There is a waymarked trail that starts and ends at the main carpark, taking in a huge variety of sights along the way.

The track of the old railway runs above the carpark; from here a short walk brings you into a strange landscape with abandoned quarries on your left and a platform of grey shale on your right. The material under your feet is slag left from the burning and leaching of the shale. This produced the precious liquor that was then channeled down to the works in the carpark area.

4 The alum works were on the site of the carpark at the north end of Sandsend village.

1 North of Sandsend beach the cliffs are mainly made of Whitby Mudstone, including Alum Shale and Jet Rock.

Cliff erosion

The cliffs at Sandsend Ness are a wonderful example of the action of sea and rain on layers of hard and soft rock. The cliff is high because the hard cap of Middle Jurassic sandstone is resistant to erosion from above. But the soft shales beneath have been washed down into a slope.

At the foot of the slope the sea has eaten away at the shales, forming a wave-cut scar and a low vertical cliff. The holes in the cliff are jet-holes, left by miners digging for the valuable mineral.

The profile of the cliffs all the way along the Dinosaur Coast show the effects of natural erosion and human exploitation of minerals such as alum, ironstone, jet, coal and cement.

Jet

The area around Whitby is famous for its jet, with workshops and jewellery shops being a long tradition. Jet is fossilised wood from araucaria or monkey puzzle trees. The trees grew on these shores, fell into the nearby sea, and were preserved in the mud on the seafloor. The wood was fossilised as a dark brown mineral which polishes to a lustrous deep black shine. The Jet Rock is a layer within the Whitby Mudstone formation and was mined wherever it was accessible, particularly around Whitby. From the shoreline at Sandsend the jet holes are clearly visible, with the pale grey alum shales above and the alum quarries in the distance. Jet jewellery was popular with Victorians and has become fashionable again thanks to stunning modern designs.

❷ The old alum quarries at Sandsend give a good section through the local geology. Above the grey flaky alum shales the line of the hard blocky Dogger Formation marks the transition to the sandstones of the Middle Jurassic that lie above. The Dogger is a feature of the cliffs all the way south to Robin Hood's Bay. The quarries, now closed for around 150 years, are being reclaimed by natural vegetation and this area is a haven for wildlife.

Dactylioceras

Harpoceras

Hildoceras

TEES
ltburn-by-the-Sea
Loftus
gh
sborough
Whitby
R Esk
Robin Hood's Bay
AR AND
ELAND
Goathland

The two most popular places for visitors to the Dinosaur Coast are also brilliant for fossils and geology in general. Whitby is founded on a geological fault, its cliffs and beaches are fascinating and it has long been the centre of the jet trade. Whitby Museum has wonderful collection of fossils, including giant reptiles, set in a park with its own Jurassic Garden. Robin Hood's Bay attracts fossil collectors from all over the world, and the coast between these two is made of a stunning section of Jurassic strata.

23

Whitby

The most picturesque small seaside town in England, Whitby owes its spectacular situation to the rocks of the Dinosaur Coast. The River Esk runs along a geological fault that cuts through the harbour. But the river has run on its present course only since the last ice age, so the gorge at its mouth is still narrow and steep. Add to that the numerous fossils found on its cliffs and beaches, and the fascinating rocks in its cliffs, and Whitby really is a geological town.

East cliff

The cliffs on either side of Whitby harbour look completely different from each other. The high vertical cliffs on the east side are made of thin bands of grey shales and sandstones. Lower Jurassic shales at the base are capped by rocks of the Middle Jurassic, formed when this area was a huge river delta. This section was formed in one of the more stagnant areas of the delta and so the rocks are dark and grey in colour, in contrast with those on the west side of the river. Whitby's famous abbey stands on top of the east cliff. The cliff is being slowly eroded as the sea eats away at the soft shales at its base. Boulders have been placed at the foot of the cliff to slow the erosion.

West cliff

The rocks overlooking the west beach and on Khyber Pass are thick layers of blocky yellow sandstones. This is a marked contrast to the grey rocks of the east cliff.

① The hard Dogger bed stands out one third of the way up the East cliff, marking the junction between Lower and Middle Jurassic rocks.

❷ The pale yellow colour of the rocks on the west side is similar to beach sand and is caused by high levels of oxygen in a clear channel of water within the Middle Jurassic delta.

❸ Whitby Abbey was originally founded in 657AD; the present structure dates from the 13th century and was abandoned in the 16th-century Dissolution of the Monasteries.

❹ Whitby Museum, with its impressive doorway, is in Pannett Park at the top of town on the west side.

Whitby Museum

Originally founded in 1823, Whitby Literary and Philosophical Society runs one of the most delightful museums in Britain. Full of strange, quirky and scary objects, the museum also has a world-class collection of Jurassic fossils including its famous giant sea reptiles. The collection of ammonites was a foundation stone in the development of fossils for fixing the ages of rock strata. The museum is in Pannett Park, which has its very own Jurassic garden.

Ammonites

The town of Whitby has always been associated with ammonites. By legend St Hilda, the founder of Whitby Abbey in the seventh century, turned the local snakes to stone. For years locals made a living selling 'snakestones' to visitors. Ammonites even ended up on the town's crest.

2 Ammonites are used on this symbol of Yorkshire's Heritage Coast.

1 The mouth of the Esk provides one of the few safe refuges for shipping on this coast. The steep streets and long narrow harbour were created by the Esk cutting down through the hard Middle Jurassic sandstones into the soft shales beneath.

3 The Jurassic Garden in Pannett Park is full of plants that thrived in this region in the Jurassic period including gingkoes, tree ferns and conifers. The path through the garden shows the rock formations of the Dinosaur Coast together with their fossils.

3 Welcome to The Jurassic Garden
Take a step back in time...

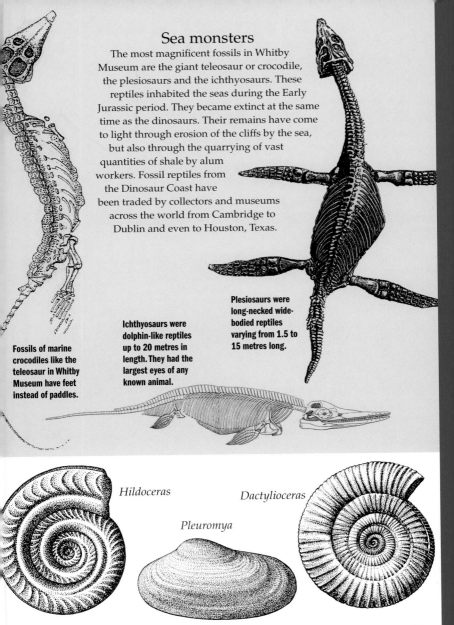

Sea monsters

The most magnificent fossils in Whitby Museum are the giant teleosaur or crocodile, the plesiosaurs and the ichthyosaurs. These reptiles inhabited the seas during the Early Jurassic period. They became extinct at the same time as the dinosaurs. Their remains have come to light through erosion of the cliffs by the sea, but also through the quarrying of vast quantities of shale by alum workers. Fossil reptiles from the Dinosaur Coast have been traded by collectors and museums across the world from Cambridge to Dublin and even to Houston, Texas.

Plesiosaurs were long-necked wide-bodied reptiles varying from 1.5 to 15 metres long.

Ichthyosaurs were dolphin-like reptiles up to 20 metres in length. They had the largest eyes of any known animal.

Fossils of marine crocodiles like the teleosaur in Whitby Museum have feet instead of paddles.

Hildoceras

Dactylioceras

Pleuromya

Saltwick to Hawsker

This isolated section of coast was once a hive of industry with workers extracting alum, jet and even coal from the cliffs and scars. The shoreline is accessible with care, and is full of geological and historical interest with fossils available in the loose rocks on the scar. The strata in this section are gently folded with different rocks coming into view, making it especially interesting for geologists.

Saltwick Bay

The bay just south of Whitby has a remarkable amount of geological history in a small area. **Only explore this area on a falling tide, and if you are fit enough to tackle a relatively steep climb.** The bay is bounded by Saltwick Nab to the northwest and Black Nab to the southeast. Both stacks have been isolated by quarrying and processing of alum on the headlands. The centre of the bay is made of glacial drift that fills the valley cut by Saltwick Beck; the beck makes a mud-filled channel that cuts through the scar and out to the sea. This marks the bottom level of the alum shales.

The rock strata between Saltwick

❷ From above Saltwick Nab and its headland reveal how they were formed. The red stone is slag from the roasting of alum shale.

and Whitby go through gentle folds. These bring rocks bearing alum and jet near to the shore from where they were shipped.

Black Nab stands isolated on the southeast end of Saltwick Bay. Quarrying and erosion have cut off the stack from the headland.

1 Seen from the shore Saltwick Nab is now a double stack cut off by the sea from the headland. The Nab is a landmark on the coast but its shape is continually changing as it is battered by the wind and sea.

Alum

Signs of the old alum industry are all around Saltwick Nab. Regular blocks of sandstone on the scar are the remnants of a quay built for alum ships, there are abandoned alum quarries in the cliff and the remains of soaking pits in the scar, while piles of red-coloured burnt shale are slowly being washed away by the sea.

4 This huge bowl behind Saltwick Nab is an old alum quarry. The cliff at the edge of the quarry shows the transition from grey shales to yellow sandstone blocks of the Middle Jurassic rocks above. Here, as elsewhere, the boundary is marked by the Dogger formation.

1 At Jump Down Bight, between Saltwick and Whitby, a downward fold in the strata brings the Dogger formation right down to the shoreline. The upper surface of the Dogger is exposed as the rocks above were mined for coal.

Cliff falls and fossils

There are continual rock falls from the vertical cliffs so there are plenty of interesting rocks and fossils loose on the scar. Large blocks of Middle Jurassic sandstone carry plant fossils and dinosaur footprints. In the scar itself ammonites and belemnites from the shales of the Whitby Mudstone are quite common.

Hawsker Bottoms

From Saltwick to Robin Hood's Bay the cliffs are vertical and the shoreline is accessible only at low tide. At Hawsker Bottoms the strata begin to lift towards the dome at Robin Hood's Bay. The base of the cliffs is Cleveland Ironstone, with Staithes Sandstone and Redcar Mudstone appearing further south. Ammonites and bivalves are common.

2 The scar at Saltwick Bay is made of shale from the Whitby Mudstone formation. The flat even surface is made by waves wearing away soft shales with level bedding planes. There are similar surfaces at Saltburn, Sandsend and Scarborough.

Reading the landscape

The Dinosaur Coast gives lots of clues to the rock types in its cliffs and scars. Rocks are different colours, ranging from yellow sandstones to orange ironstone to grey shale, cream limestone and white chalk. Some strata are thick and blocky while others are thin and crumbly. Another clue comes with the shape of the landscape itself. A change in slope often means

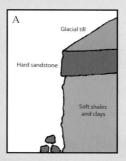

a change in rock type. Cliff profiles like this [A] show layers of soft rock at the shoreline being worn away by the sea to make an overhang of the hard layers above. That combination makes a vertical face. The slope on top indicates a layer of glacial mud being washed down by rain from above.

The same rock profile inland [B] is different because the lower soft shales are washed down from above giving a sharp slope under the vertical face of the hard rocks above.

3 Ammonites like this Dactylioceras are embedded in the scar at Saltwick Bay.

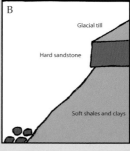

4 A belemnite standing out on the Saltwick scar.

Robin Hood's Bay

One of the most beautiful sights on the British coast, this wide sweeping bay is a geological marvel. A great uplift occurred in the Cretaceous period that created a dome with rock strata stacked on top of each other in hemispheres. The remnant of the dome is a series of circular strata sweeping round the bay. The same uplift brought the Redcar Mudstone, the oldest Jurassic formation, up to sea level. Well known for its fossils the bay is regularly picked over, so this is a place to browse and enjoy rather than collect.

❶ Tectonic movements are continually reshaping the earth's surface. At Robin Hood's Bay the Jurassic rocks were forced upwards into a dome before being eroded to give a spectacular circular shape to the beds.

❷ The village of Bay was built into the gully cut by streams; in recent decades it has spread along the plateau above.

❶

Ammonite time zones

The Jurassic period is divided into time zones, each defined by a particular ammonite species. Because of the eroded dome structure, the rocks on the scar at Robin Hood's Bay are laid out horizontal ammonite zones. The oldest zone is the Semicostatum zone which outcrops below low water in the centre of the bay; beds are successively younger on either side, with the youngest Daveoi zone, outcropping at North Cheek. Each zone covers about one million years.

The whole of the Jurassic period is divided into ammonite-based time zones. This is more reliable than using rock formations for dating as rock types vary from one location to another.

Zone fossils

Ammonites are perfect as zone fossils. Many species had a relatively short existence and because they were free-floating they spread rapidly over a wide area. These are the ammonite zones at Robin Hood's Bay (below).

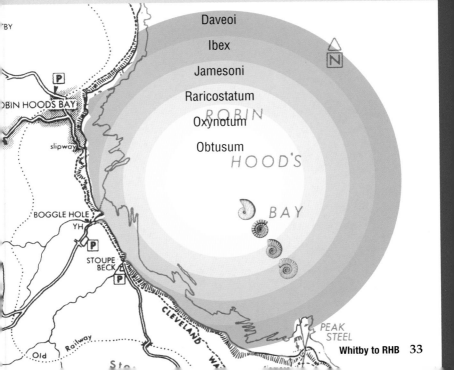

Glacial till

The bowl formed by the erosion of the Robin Hood's Bay dome makes a wonderful natural amphitheatre. On the landward side this created a low-lying area that was filled with glacial mud during the last ice age. This till is clearly visible in the cliffs south of the village and at Boggle, Stoup Beck and south towards Ravenscar. A strip of land all along the coast is covered in till, which gives rolling hills and green pastures. The ice sheets did not reach the moorland, which is covered with a thin, acid soil. The land above the centre of the bay is stepped with a lower plateau made of Redcar Mudstone and glacial till. Further back harder rocks of the Staithes Sandstone and Cleveland Ironstone formations form another steep escarpment that wraps around the bay. This

1 At Boggle Hole the beck has cut down through glacial till and Jurassic rocks to form a steep valley. The narrow gorge shows that this is a new course for the beck, possibly made since the ice ages.

slope continues up through alum shales and is capped by the Dogger and hard sandstones of the Middle Jurassic.

2 Great slabs of Redcar Mudstone form the horizontal wave-cut scar at Robin Hood's Bay. This huge exposure has allowed geologists to plot time zones from the ammonite fossils in the scar.

❸ The cliff at Boggle Hole shows glacial till piled on top of level layers of Redcar Mudstone.

Middle Jurassic Sandstone — Dogger formation

Mudstone and Alum Shale

Cleveland Ironstone

Staithes Sandstone — Glacial till and boulder clay

Redcar Mudstone

❹ Glacial till filled in the low-lying space around the edges of the rock dome as ice sheets pushed in from the North Sea. The cliffs between Bay village and Boggle Hole are nearly all glacial till.

Peak to Scarbor

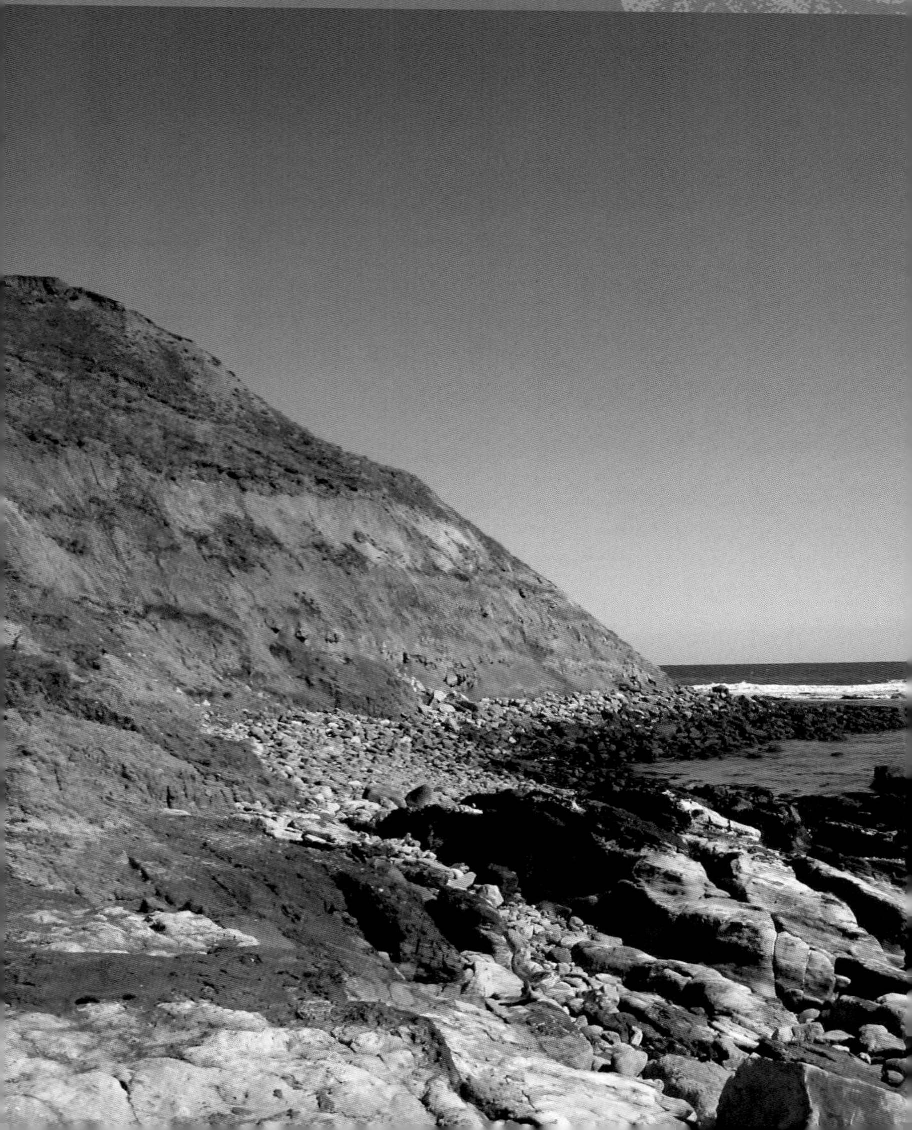

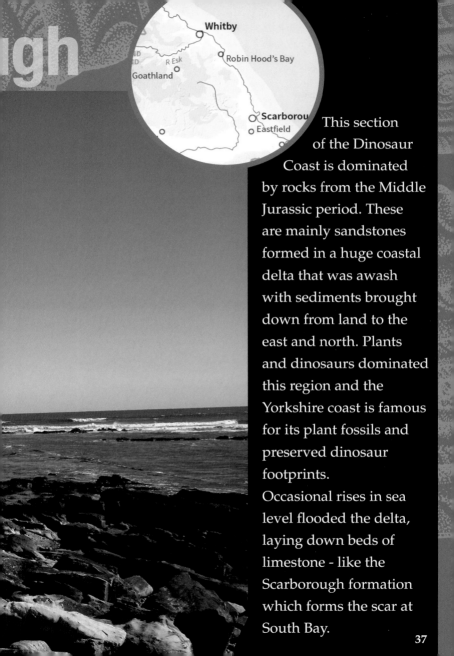

Whitby

Robin Hood's Bay

R Esk

Goathland

Scarborou

Eastfield

This section of the Dinosaur Coast is dominated by rocks from the Middle Jurassic period. These are mainly sandstones formed in a huge coastal delta that was awash with sediments brought down from land to the east and north. Plants and dinosaurs dominated this region and the Yorkshire coast is famous for its plant fossils and preserved dinosaur footprints.

Occasional rises in sea level flooded the delta, laying down beds of limestone - like the Scarborough formation which forms the scar at South Bay.

The great headland at Ravenscar owes its prominence to a major geological fault. The Peak Fault has a throw of around 90 metres and brings younger rocks to the shoreline. It also brings hard sandstones which form the resistant cap of this dramatic headland. South of the headland a unique section exposes the Peak Mudstone and Blea Wyke formations. These are the most southerly of the Lower Jurassic rocks on the Dinosaur Coast. From here to Scarborough we encounter Middle and then Upper Jurassic rocks.

Peak Fault

This massive fault brings about a major change in the geology of the Dinosaur Coast. The fault runs roughly north to south and crosses the coast at the Peak headland below Ravenscar. A series of similar faults created the Peak Trough, where huge amounts of sediment were deposited in Jurassic times. Movements along the faults of the Peak Trough lasted from before the Jurassic period right through to the Tertiary, 100 million years or so later.

Ravenscar

Once the coastal railway was built in 1885 a resort town was planned at Ravenscar. Streets were laid out, sewers were built and prospective house buyers were lured with posters and adverts. But the exposed position and the long walk down to the shore put people off. Only a few houses were built and Ravenscar remains a natural headland with spectacular views over the full breadth of Robin Hood's Bay.

❶ Ravenscar headland towers over the southeastern end of Robin Hood's Bay. The Peak Fault cuts through the headland creating a double set of cliffs.

Middle Jurassic
Dogger
Blea Wyke Sandstone
Whitby Mudstone
Staithes Sandstone
Redcar Mudstone

② Immediately to the west of the fault hard Staithes Sandstone sits above softer Redcar Mudstone.

④ A sketch map of the geology shows how the Peak Fault has displaced the key Dogger bed, bringing younger rocks to outcrop at the coast. The Peak Steel is a slice of hard Staithes Sandstone.

③ On the east side of the Peak Fault hard blocky sandstones of the Middle Jurassic form the towering headland at Ravenscar.

Peak Steel

The Peak Fault actually divides at the coast, forming a spectacular landform. The Peak Steel is the piece of Staithes Sandstone that lies between the two forks of the fault. Because it is harder than the Redcar and Whitby Mudstone on either side, the steel sticks out into the sea like a giant snout. Seals and seabirds are often seen here and on the surrounding rocks in this stunning location.

1 The Peak Steel is a narrow nose of hard Staithes Sandstone that sits between two branches of the Peak Fault. On the west side the same rock sits 30 metres or so higher.

2 Undercliffs or Beast cliffs are a feature of this part of the coast. This shelf shows the junction between rock types and a notable collection of flora.

Blea Wyke

The shoreline south of the Peak headland should only be visited on a falling tide. This area is of great interest geologically as it shows off a series of Lower Jurassic formations from the Jet Rock, Alum Shale, Peak Mudstone, Fox Cliff Siltstone and Blea Wyke sandstone before reaching the Dogger, which marks the top of the Lower Jurassic.

Fossil bivalves and ammonites are fairly common in this area but the cliffs are particularly dangerous due to rock falls.

Alum

Alum was quarried and processed in huge quantities along this coast until the 1870s. Remains of the quarries and works stretch all the way from Hummersea to Peak. Thanks to the quarries alongside the old railway and the well-preserved alum works, Ravenscar is the best location to see the full picture. It's easy to see why this was such a good location, with the quarries above the large plateau that fringes the bay. The finished alum was shipped out after being taken down to the beach below.

❸ The remains of the Peak alum works lie on the plateau below the quarries, allowing mineral-rich solutions to be channeled downhill. The finished alum was taken down the cliffs to ships waiting on the shore. This is the best preserved alum works on the coast with the complete alum story told on boards at the site.

❹ The spectacular quarry face shows grey soft alum shale topped by a band of hard yellow Dogger. Blocks of Dogger and Middle Jurassic sandstone litter the quarry floor which is made up of shale and slag from the roasting of the alum. The sandstone blocks contain fossils of horsetail ferns or equisetum.

The huge Brickyards Alum Quarry is a Nature Reserve well worth exploring.

Hayburn Wyke to Scalby Mills

The hard sandstones and limestones formed in the Middle Jurassic period dominate this stretch of coast, forming high cliffs and a hard to access shoreline. The exceptions are the small bays at Hayburn and Cloughton Wykes and the long stretch of scar at Scalby Bay. Here the boulder-strewn shores and cliffs show magnificent examples of internal rock structures, plant fossils and dinosaur footprints.

Hayburn Wyke

The beautiful woods and cove are accessible from the Cleveland Way footpath and the old Scarborough to Whitby railway. During the Middle Jurassic this area was, for most of the time, a huge coastal delta with freshwater sandstone being formed in clear water channels, and occasional darker rocks in the stagnant marshes.

Plant fossils

The plant fossils from the Yorkshire coast are of world scientific

1 Hayburn Wyke has been popular with day-trippers from Scarborough since Victorian times. Charabancs and then the railway brought visitors to the hotel that lies just above the Nature Reserve.

2 Hayburn Beck runs over a platform of hard Middle Jurassic sandstones. On the way it exposes beds containing notable plant fossils.

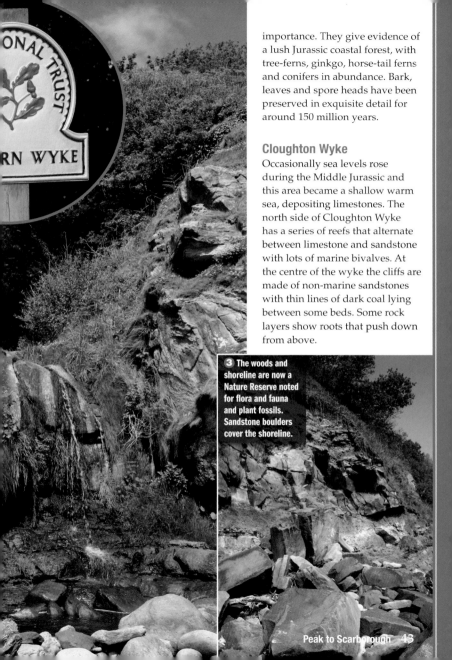

importance. They give evidence of a lush Jurassic coastal forest, with tree-ferns, ginkgo, horse-tail ferns and conifers in abundance. Bark, leaves and spore heads have been preserved in exquisite detail for around 150 million years.

Cloughton Wyke

Occasionally sea levels rose during the Middle Jurassic and this area became a shallow warm sea, depositing limestones. The north side of Cloughton Wyke has a series of reefs that alternate between limestone and sandstone with lots of marine bivalves. At the centre of the wyke the cliffs are made of non-marine sandstones with thin lines of dark coal lying between some beds. Some rock layers show roots that push down from above.

3 The woods and shoreline are now a Nature Reserve noted for flora and fauna and plant fossils. Sandstone boulders cover the shoreline.

Channel splay sandstones

Some bands of sandstone at Cloughton Wyke are completely uniform with no bedding and little gradation of grain size. These channel splay sandstones were formed when the delta was suddenly flooded sending huge amounts of silt onto the surrounding land. The silt was often around 50 cm deep. The resulting sandstone is excellent for building as it cuts evenly and doesn't fracture along bedding or cleavage planes. Cloughton sandstone is used in buildings all around this area, including most of the houses on the village high street.

1 This small area of cliff face at Cloughton Wyke shows a huge variety of rocks, from uniform splay sandstones to coal beds to thin bedded sands, and topped off by a layer of glacial till.

2 This bed of channel splay sandstone, created in a single flood, is very uniform with no internal features. This makes it ideal building material.

3 The Middle Jurassic is famous for its plant fossils, and it also has beds of coal which used to be mined right across the region. Notice the plant roots extending down into the lower layers of sand.

4 Scalby Beck reaches the sea at Scalby Mills, cutting a gorge through Middle Jurassic rocks. The bays north of here show dinosaur footprints on the scar and some fascinating sedimentary structures.

Dinosaur footprints

There is plenty of evidence that dinosaurs lived on the Yorkshire coast. Footprints left in mud and sandbanks and preserved as infills are commonly found on the shoreline. Prints appear on the scar as the sea wears away the surrounding rock; they then get worn away in turn, so the prints themselves are continually changing. Footprints also appear on blocks that have fallen from the cliffs and flipped over. Footprints tell the size, weight and species of dinosaur; they also tell us if they were walking or running and how fast.

5 In the Jurassic period this was a coastal delta. Just as now, the tides left ripple marks and some of these have been preserved as the sand hardened into rock.

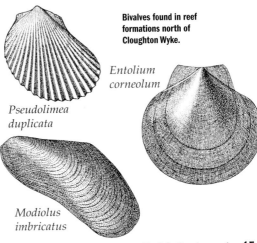

Bivalves found in reef formations north of Cloughton Wyke.

Pseudolimea duplicata

Entolium corneolum

Modiolus imbricatus

Scarborough

Scarborough has arguably the finest setting of any seaside town in England. The twin bays are magnificent sweeps of sand separated by a spectacular headland bearing the ruins of the castle. All this is here because of a series of geological faults that brought the hard rocks of the castle headland up against softer surrounding rocks. The South Bay also has wonderful exposures of Middle Jurassic rocks with both marine fossils and dinosaur footprints. Scarborough also has a crucial place in the history of geology, a story told in the beautiful displays of the Rotunda Museum.

Castle headland

The Castle headland is the reason for the town's existence. A major geological fault has dropped this massive stack of rocks down by around 60 metres. The rocks themselves are identical to those on the top of Oliver's Mount, which stands high above the town.

The headland is topped by hard layers of Malton Oolite and Lower Calcareous Grit – these are the pale blocky rocks that stand out near the top. Underneath these is a thick layer of soft grey Oxford Clay. When this gets worn away by rainwater, it undercuts the hard layers above and great blocks come

❸ A Y-shaped fault cuts across the neck of Castle Hill. The rocks on the hill are younger and harder than the rocks just inland.

❶ Hard layers of oolite and grit form the cap of Castle Hill. Soft Oxford Clay forms the long slope; at sea level hard sandstones protect the headland from erosion.

❷ One branch of the fault cuts diagonally across the slope above Scarborough's North Bay. The softer rocks on the neck of the headland have been worn away far more than the hard rocks of Castle Hill.

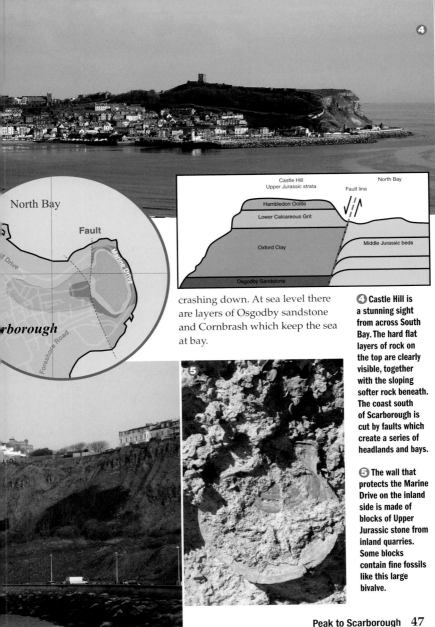

North Bay

Fault

rborough

Castle Hill
Upper Jurassic strata

North Bay

Fault line

Hambledon Oolite

Lower Calcareous Grit

Oxford Clay

Middle Jurassic beds

Osgodby Sandstone

crashing down. At sea level there are layers of Osgodby sandstone and Cornbrash which keep the sea at bay.

❹ **Castle Hill is a stunning sight from across South Bay. The hard flat layers of rock on the top are clearly visible, together with the sloping softer rock beneath. The coast south of Scarborough is cut by faults which create a series of headlands and bays.**

❺ **The wall that protects the Marine Drive on the inland side is made of blocks of Upper Jurassic stone from inland quarries. Some blocks contain fine fossils like this large bivalve.**

Peak to Scarborough 47

South Bay dinosaurs

The rocks to the south of the castle are from the Middle Jurassic period. Dinosaurs lived along this coast and their footprints are clearly visible, if you know where to look! Here the prints are preserved in section, so you are looking at them from the side. The prints are embedded in the rocks alongside the path running south from the Spa.

South Bay scar

Heading south from the town beach you will notice the sand turning to rock in some places. This is the Scarborough Limestone formation. The presence of limestone in Middle Jurassic rocks shows that there were occasional rises in sea level, making this a shallow sub-tropical sea. Sea levels then dropped again returning the coast to a delta with plants and land animals.

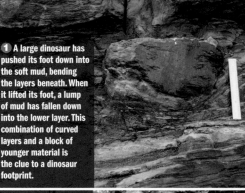

1 A large dinosaur has pushed its foot down into the soft mud, bending the layers beneath. When it lifted its foot, a lump of mud has fallen down into the lower layer. This combination of curved layers and a block of younger material is the clue to a dinosaur footprint.

2 This section of scar in South Bay shows bright red nodules of ironstone. This is the White Nab formation, made of a hard iron carbonate known as chamosite.

3 These sandstones were formed in river channels and on sandbanks. The shapes of the rock beds reflect the currents flowing through the sand. Here a curved channel sandstone rests on top of a series of flat beds.

South Bay cliffs

To the south of the Holbeck landslip the paved path drops down onto a scar of Middle Jurassic iron-rich limestone. The cliffs are mainly sandstones that show a variety of internal structures.

Rotunda Museum

William Smith was the first person to recognize that particular fossils occur in certain rock strata. In 1815 he published the first map of the geology of England and Wales, and in 1824 he came to live in Scarborough. The local gentry were fascinated by geology and Smith, known as the Father of English Geology, persuaded them to build a new museum. The Rotunda was opened in 1829; a major refit in 2008 brought it back to its former glory.

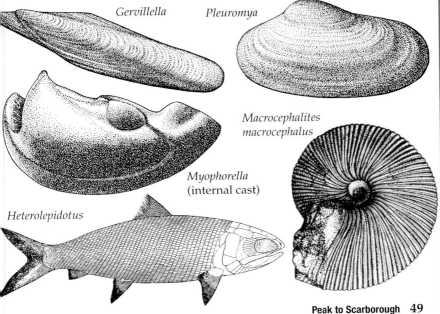

Gervillella

Pleuromya

Macrocephalites macrocephalus

Myophorella (internal cast)

Heterolepidotus

Cayton to Flambo

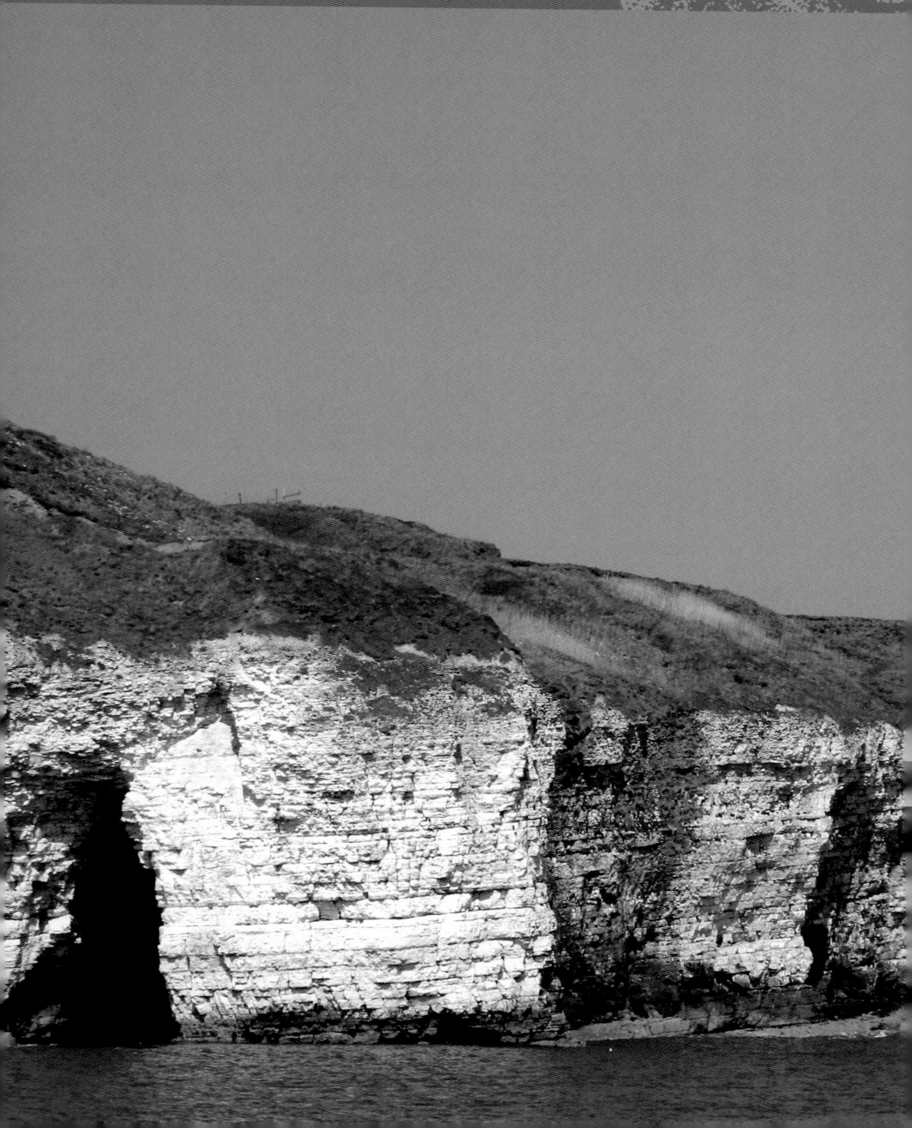

The southern part of the Dinosaur Coast is a different kind of seascape. The high cliffs and narrow inlets of the north give way to wide sweeping bays guarded by dramatic headlands. A series of faults running down the coast brings hard and soft rocks against each other at sea level. This contrast creates a series of sandy beaches at Cornelian, Cayton and Gristhorpe bays, as well as the huge sweep of Filey sands. This seascape finally gives way to the towering chalk cliffs of Flamborough Head.

Cayton Bay

A series of faults has created hard headlands and soft bays along this stretch of coast. White Nab, Osgodby Point, Yons Nab and Filey Brigg enclose a series of picturesque strands, each with a fascinating geological story. The faults make that story more complicated than further north and they bring a huge variety of rocks and fossils within easy reach.

2

Cornelian Bay

This small sandy bay just south of Scarborough is a delightful spot. Bounded by the headlands of White Nab and Osgodby Point, Cornelian Bay shows a fascinating range of Middle Jurassic rocks. At the north end the limestone of the Scarborough formation and the White Nab ironstone are brought to beach level by an upward arch of the rocks. Towards the south of the bay a fault brings the distinctive Cornbrash rock down to beach level. Immediately on top is the soft grey Oxford Clay.

Cayton Bay

The peculiar headland at Osgodby Point marks the north end of Cayton Bay. A fault cuts across the back of the headland isolating a hard slab of rock known as the Millepore Bed at sea level. The cliffs of the bay are a mix of Jurassic rocks and recent glacial mud left by the last ice age. The

2 The Oxford Clay outcrops in the cliffs at Cayton Bay. It is 160 million years old, but is soft enough to crumble in your fingers.

4

1 Cornbrash is easy to spot; the blue-grey rock is very coarse and full of fragments of fossil shells.

1

3 At Tenant's Cliff massive slabs of calcareous grit have been turned on end. The grey patch in the cliffs to the right is the underlying Oxford Clay.

mud carries lots of pebbles and rocks, many from Scotland and the Lake District, which end up as pebbles on these shores. Walking south across the bay you pass a section of red glacial mud, before a narrow section of soft grey Oxford Clay. Next to this is the pale gritstone of Tenant's Cliff. This rock is from the Lower Calcareous Grit formation that lies right across the Tabular Hills from Oliver's Mount to Helmsley.

Red Cliff

South of the waterworks building at Cayton Bay there is more glacial mud in the cliffs, before you reach the massive face of Red Cliff. Here hard calcareous grit sits on top of softer clay, with a thin layer of Cornbrash at beach level. Follow the beds round the bay and a diagonal near-vertical fault is clearly visible. Here younger rocks from the Middle Jurassic have been pushed upwards.

4 At Osgodby Point the hard rock at sea-level protects the softer rocks and glacial mud behind it.

5 This closer view shows the blocky sandstones at Osgodby Point.

❶ The high point at Yon's Nab has been isolated by a major geological fault cutting across the headland.

❷ This massive wedge of glacial mud has slid down the cliff below Knipe Point and ended up on the beach at Cayton Bay. The tree stumps on the beach are evidence of previous mud slides.

Mud slides

There is a thick layer of glacial mud found on top of many of the cliffs on the Dinosaur Coast. At the end of the last ice age, 11,000 years ago, an ice sheet up to a mile thick melted, leaving a huge amount of soft debris. This is washed away by the sea from below and by rain from above. A thick layer of glacial mud lies all along the coast, see map below, providing fertile farming land.

Yons Nab and Gristhorpe Bay

The Middle Jurassic strata follow in regular succession round the headland to Gristhorpe Bay. As the rocks dip south, Upper Jurassic rocks appear in the upper part of the cliffs. Boulders from these strata are scattered across the scar and contain numerous fossils.

Plant fossils from the Gristhorpe bed are famous in Jurassic geology. The Upper Jurassic rocks above the plant beds contain ammonites and myophorella bivalves.

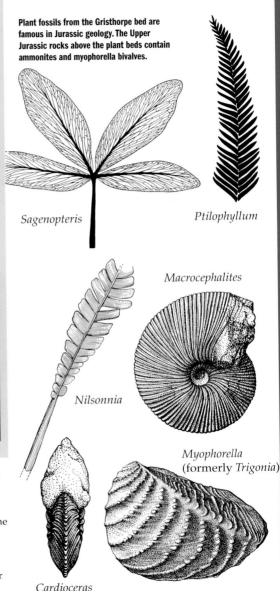

Sagenopteris

Ptilophyllum

Macrocephalites

Nilsonnia

Myophorella (formerly *Trigonia*)

Cardioceras

Filey Bay

The bay at Filey is one of the finest stretches of sand in Britain. Running eight miles south from the Brigg the bay is a spectacular sight and is full of geological interest. The Brigg is a major landmark created by another geological fault, this time bringing a sliver of hard grit to sea level. The remainder of the bay comprises rocks, mainly clays, from the younger Cretaceous period, topped by more glacial mud. Toward the southern end is an outcrop of black Cretaceous clay known as the Speeton Clay. Beyond that are the great chalk cliffs of Flamborough.

Filey Brigg

The Brigg is a long outcrop of hard Upper Jurassic rock. Most of the rock is a calcareous grit, similar to the rock that dominates the Tabular Hills. On the north side of the Brigg there are also beds of limestone from the Hambleton Oolite formation. A series of faults have brought these hard rocks against softer clays, so leaving a long nose-like structure stretching 500 metres into the sea.

❷

❶ From the south the Brigg looks like a narwhal with a big head and a narrow tusk. The 'head', known as Carr Naze, is made of red glacial till – the shelf of rocks beneath stop this soft mud being washed into the sea. Filey Bay has red cliffs made of till and mud.

❷ The long nose of Filey Brigg is made of Birdsall grit. This is a small rock formation that occurs locally. This hard sandstone makes up the southern side of the Brigg. This is the southern limit of the Jurassic rocks of the Dinosaur Coast; south from here the rocks are from the Cretaceous period.

❸ On the south side of the Brigg the hard sandstones of the Birdsall grit protect the soft mud that sits on top.

Clay

South from here the cliffs of the bay are mainly soft glacial mudstones. This part of the coast, and the area inland, sees the transition from the sandstones and limestones of the Upper Jurassic to the chalk beds of the Cretaceous period. In between are a series of clay beds which are of great geological interest. The Kimmeridge Clay is up to 300 metres thick and underlies the flat Vale of Pickering. Kimmeridge Clay contains lots of fossils and is the source rock for North Sea oil.

❹ The cliffs on the north side of the Brigg are from the Upper Jurassic Corallian formation. They outcrop at Scarborough Castle, Oliver's Mount and all the way along the Tabular Hills to Helmsley.

❺ A reconstruction of the Roman signal station at Filey Brigg.

Cayton to Flamborough 57

Towards Bempton

At the south end of Filey Bay the first signs of chalk become visible. The strip of sand gets thinner and the cliffs get higher, so the shoreline becomes inaccessible. You can get a good view of the cliffs at the RSPB reserve at Bempton. Here gannets, puffins, kittiwakes, guillemots and razorbills nest on the stacks, ledges, and in burrows in the sheer cliff faces. The gannets' favourite site is on top of a chalk stack giving clifftop walkers a fine view of the birds and the chalk rocks.

Speeton Clay

In the low cliff, a mile or so south of Reighton Gap, is an outcrop of black sticky clay, distinct from the red mud of the surrounding ice age deposits. This is the Speeton Clay, which was formed during the Cretaceous period. The clay is rich in fossils, mainly belemnites, but also bivalves and ammonites. It is well known to local geologists who have formed the 'Friends of the Speeton Clay'.

Trace fossils

Creatures leave their marks in rocks, and these can remain for millions of years. Animals make burrows in sand and mud, these are often filled in with different material. When the sand hardens into rock the burrows stand out on the surface because they are harder. The burrows

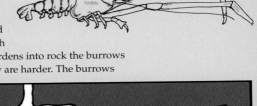

preserved on Filey Brigg were made by the Thalassinoides shrimp, above. The drawing, right, shows typical crab burrows.

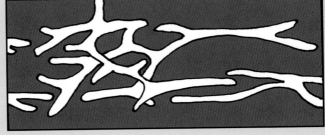

Fossils from the Speeton Clay formation.

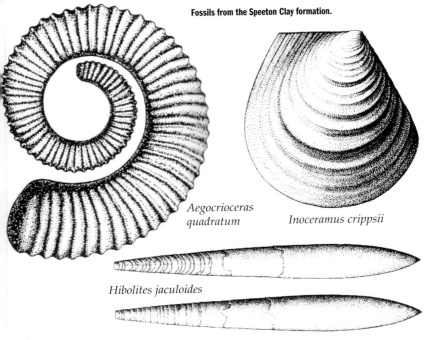

Aegocrioceras quadratum

Inoceramus crippsii

Hibolites jaculoides

Flamborough

Flamborough Head is one of the great landmarks of the British coast. Jutting 8 miles out into the North Sea, the towering stacks of chalk create vertical cliffs over 130 metres high. The chalk has been weathered into stacks, arches and sea caves, while the cliffs themselves are full of geological features. The area is famous for its seabirds and the shoreline is easily accessible via a series of beautiful coves or landings.

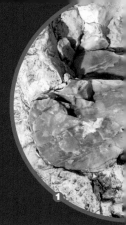

Thornwick Bay and North Landing

These small bays on the north side of the headland give a shoreline view of the great stacks of chalk. From here it is easy to see that the chalk is not uniform. Some bands contain nodules of grey flint, and occasional beds are coloured red from iron. There are also beds of marl, a mixture of chalk, silt and mud. These different beds can be easily traced across the cliffs and are used as marker beds around the headland.

Selwicks Bay

The main feature of this lovely bay, out on the tip of Flamborough Head, is a zone of intense folding and faulting which shows up clearly in the cliff face. The earth movements that created the Alps beginning 50 million years ago, had effects across northern Europe, including faults that run across the Wolds and out to Flamborough. The rocks here were first squeezed, then pulled apart leaving great lines of cracking and slumps in the strata across the cliffs.

❶ Hard flint nodules commonly form in chalk rocks.

❷ Thornwick Nab is a beautiful headland continually eroded by the sea, with sea caves, stacks and arches being created and worn away. The layer of brown glacial till on top of the white chalk stands out clearly on the nab.

Flamborough Head

Chalk is often thought to be a soft porous rock but a band of harder chalk runs across the northern edge of the Wolds and creates the headland at Flamborough. Most chalk is poor building material as it absorbs water which can then freeze, shattering the stone. But hard Flamborough chalk is used, for example, in the old lighthouse.

South Landing and Sewerby Steps

It's possible to walk along much of the southern side of the headland at low tide. Starting at South Landing there is a continuous sequence of chalk all the way to Sewerby Steps. Fossil crinoids, bivalves and sponges are all found in the rocks along this shore, along with some brachiopods and belemnites.

❸ Most of the chalk beds are regular and close to horizontal. ❹ But a zone of intense folding has made these beds at Selwicks Bay nearly vertical.

5 The old lighthouse stands just inland from the headland. Built in 1669 from local chalk, it is the oldest complete lighthouse in the country.

Danes Dyke

In the Bronze Age a spectacular structure was built across the headland, presumably to create a defensive barrier. The dyke is a ditch and earth bank, running for 4 kilometres from sea to sea, cutting off the headland. The coast meets the end of Danes Dyke which, at this point, was made by digging out glacial mud from an old meltwater channel.

Chalk

During the Cretaceous period, which lasted from 145 to 65 million years ago, sea levels were much higher than today. Warm shallow tranquil seas covered many of the continental areas, perfect conditions for chalk deposits. Cretaceous chalk is found in many parts of the world; here in Yorkshire the chalk was more than 1500 metres deep.

At the end of the Cretaceous period the dinosaurs, ichthyosaurs and plesiosaurs, as well as the ammonites and belemnites, disappeared.

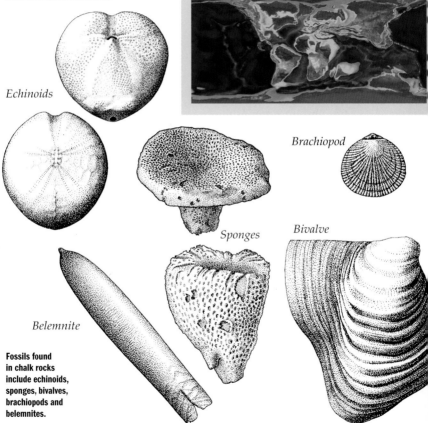

Echinoids

Brachiopod

Sponges

Bivalve

Belemnite

Fossils found in chalk rocks include echinoids, sponges, bivalves, brachiopods and belemnites.

Buried cliff

The chalk cliffs of Flamborough seem to come to a sudden end on the North Beach at Bridlington. The cliff actually continues inland following a line eastwards that marked the coastline before the last ice age. The cliffs from here to Spurn Point are made of glacial till dumped by melting ice sheets.

The chalk cliff is buried by glacial till just north of Bridlington at Sewerby. The Holderness coast, which runs south from here, is made of soft mud which erodes very rapidly.

Fossil collecting code

- The coast is beautiful but potentially dangerous. **Do not** go near cliff edges nor the base of cliffs as there are continual rock falls.
- Before walking along a shoreline always check tides and visit when the tide is falling. Take a phone and always tell someone where you are going.
- Collect fossils from loose material on the beach or scar, **do not** dig or hammer fossils from the cliffs or the scar.
- Go on organised fossil walks like those provided by Hidden Horizons: www.hiddenhorizons.co.uk

Further information

These museums all have displays on fossils, geology and mining:

Rotunda Museum, Valley Road, Scarborough

Kirkleatham Museum, Redcar

Cleveland Iron Mining Museum, Skinningrove

Staithes Heritage Centre, High Street, Staithes

Whitby Museum, Pannett Park, Whitby

For general information on the area visit the National Park Centres at Danby and Sutton Bank.

For more information on the geology of the coast see the following books:
Natural History Museum, *Mesozoic Fossils,* Revised edn, 2013
Roger Osborne, *Rocks and Landscape of the North York Moors,* NYM National Park, 2010
Roger Osborne, *The Floating Egg,* Pimlico, 1998
Peter Rawson and John Wright, *The Yorkshire Coast,* Geologists Association, 3rd edition, 2000

Acknowledgements
The publishers are grateful to Whitby Museum, North York Moors National Park, Scarborough Museums Trust, Natural History Museum and Hidden Horizons for their support.